NIGHT OF THE CRASH

Paul Blum

RISING★STARS

Rising Stars UK Ltd.
22 Grafton Street, London W1S 4EX
www.risingstars-uk.com

nasen

NASEN House, 4/5 Amber Business Village, Amber Close,
Amington, Tamworth, Staffordshire B77 4RP

Published 2008

Cover design: pentacor**big**
Illustrator: Chris King, Illustration Ltd.
Text design and typesetting: pentacor**big**
Publisher: Gill Budgell
Editor: Catherine Baker
Editorial project management: Margot O'Keeffe
Editorial consultant: Lorraine Petersen
Photos: Alamy

British Library Cataloguing in Publication Data.
A CIP record for this book is available from the British Library.

ISBN: 978-1-84680-459-5

Printed by Craft Print International Limited, Singapore

shadows

Contents

The Crash

- The Crash happened in 2021. Alien space ships crash landed on Earth.

- After The Crash, the Earth became very cold and dark.

- Now the aliens rule the world.

- The aliens have changed shape so they look like people.

- People call the aliens The Enemy.

Life after the Crash

- People are afraid.

- They do not know who is an Enemy and who is a friend.

The Firm

- The Firm keeps order on the streets.

- The Firm keeps people safe from Enemy attacks.

About Matt Merton

Matt Merton works for The Firm. He often works with Dexter. Their job is to find and kill The Enemy. They use Truth Sticks to do this.

But Matt has problems.

Matt has lost his memory. He cannot answer some big questions.

- Where has Jane, his girlfriend, gone?

- How did he get his job with The Firm?

Matt thinks The Firm is on the side of good. But is it?

chapter 1

Matt Merton sat in the bar.

Matt Merton sat in the shadows. It was late.

'What did you do on the night of The Crash, Mr Merton?' said Sam, the bar man.

'I'll tell you,' said Matt. 'But get me a coffee first.'

'With an extra shot?' said Sam.

'Yes, with an extra shot — and extra hot,'
said Matt.

Sam and Matt began to talk. They talked for a long time.

Matt looked sad. 'The night of The Crash was bad,' he said. 'It was the worst night of my life.'

'It was the worst night of all our lives,' said Sam.

chapter 2

Matt was silent. Sam told his story of The Crash.

'I was here in the bar. I heard a big bang.
I ran outside.

There were space ships everywhere.'

'I ran back inside.

Then I saw the news on the TV.'

'I was very afraid. I didn't know what to do.

But there was nothing I could do.'

'A space ship crashed into the centre of the city.

There was fire everywhere. Many people died.'

chapter 3

Matt was silent, so Sam went on speaking.

'I saw the crashed space ship. I saw the aliens.'

'I saw the aliens turn into humans.

They disappeared into the crowd.'

'I phoned my family. I wanted to make sure they were safe.

But they did not answer...'

'I ran home, but I was too late. The house was on fire. I couldn't find my family.

They had disappeared.'

chapter 4

Matt put his hand on Sam's shoulder.
'Sam, I am so sorry,' he said.

'I looked for my family everywhere,' said Sam.
'But I never found them.'

'Many people disappeared …

… It was a long night.'

'I helped save an old man.'

'I helped save a child.

I helped so many people that night. But I could not save my own family.'

'I will never forget that night,' said Matt.

'It was May. But it began to snow.'

'Now it snows all year,' said Sam.
'Always winter and never summer.'

Both men sat in silence.

'So, what did you do that night, Mr Merton?' said Sam.

'I'll tell you another time, Sam,' he said.